# I Can Draw
# THINGS THAT GO

## Parent notes:

**1** Make sure your child uses a soft pencil that can be easily erased.

**2** Encourage your child to trace over the outlines (from 1 to 4) to see how the picture comes together in simple steps.

**3** In the space below steps 1 and 2, your child can draw the picture step by step as many times as he or she likes.

**4** When ready, your child can draw the picture into the scene and complete it.

# The airplane zooms through the sky.

① **Draw the airplane's shape.**

② **Add the tail and wings.**

③ **Draw the engines.**

④ **Then add the windows.**

# Busy car!

**1** Draw two wheels.

**2** Add the car's body.

**3** Draw the windows.

**4** Then add the headlights, wheel arches and doors.

# A bus can carry lots of people.

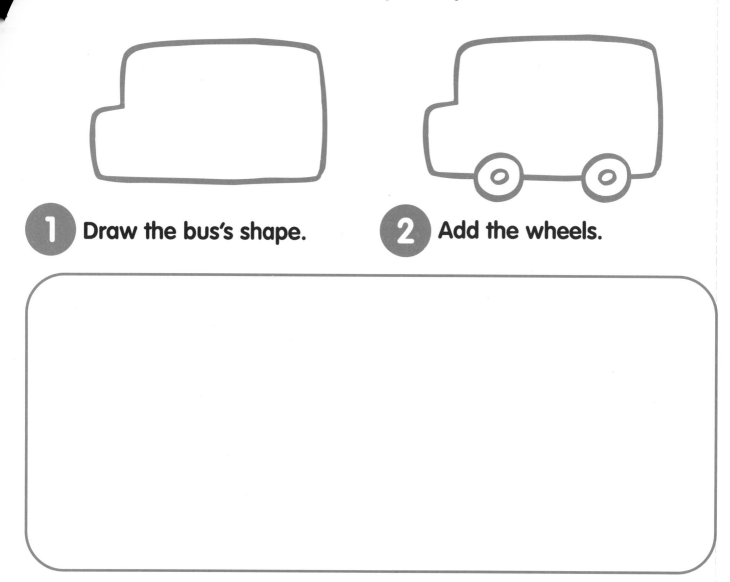

**1** Draw the bus's shape.

**2** Add the wheels.

**3** Draw the windows.

**4** Then add the headlights, wheel arches and stripe.

# How fast can you ride your bicycle?

**1** Draw the bicycle's frame.

**2** Add the wheels.

**3** Draw the handlebars.

**4** Then add the seat and pedals.

# The tractor is busy working on the farm.

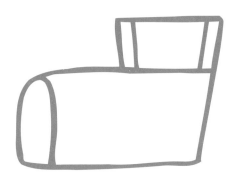

**1** Draw the tractor's shape.

**2** Add the wheels.

**3** Draw the driver's cab and engine funnel.

**4** Then add the tow bar and finishing details.

# A helicopter has spinning blades instead of wings.

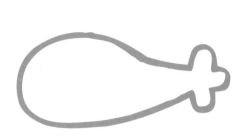

1 Draw the helicopter's shape.

2 Add four rotor blades.

3 Draw the landing skids.

4 Then add the windshield and stripes.

# How many sailboats are on the sea?

**1** Draw the boat's hull.

**2** Add the mast and flag.

**3** Draw two sails.

**4** Then add the portholes and stripes.

# This truck delivers lots of food.

**1** Draw the truck's shape.

**2** Add the wheels.

**3** Draw the driver's cab.

**4** Then add the lights, window and stripe.

# Who will win this motorcycle race?

**1** Draw the motorcycle's frame.

**2** Add the wheels.

**3** Draw the handlebar, seat and exhaust.

**4** Then add the headlight, pedals and finishing details.

# The fire truck races to the rescue.

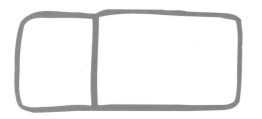

**1** Draw the fire truck's shape.

**2** Add the wheels.

**3** Draw the long ladder.

**4** Then add the lights, hose and window.

# The rocket blasts into space!

**1** Draw the rocket's shape.

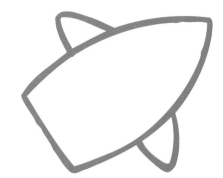

**2** Add the wings.

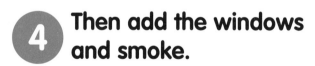

**3** Draw the nose and engine.

**4** Then add the windows and smoke.

# Here comes the train!

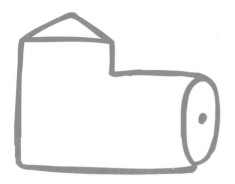

**1** Draw the train's shape.

**2** Add the wheels.

**3** Draw the window and smokestack.

**4** Then add the smoke and finishing details.

# This tanker truck can carry lots of milk.

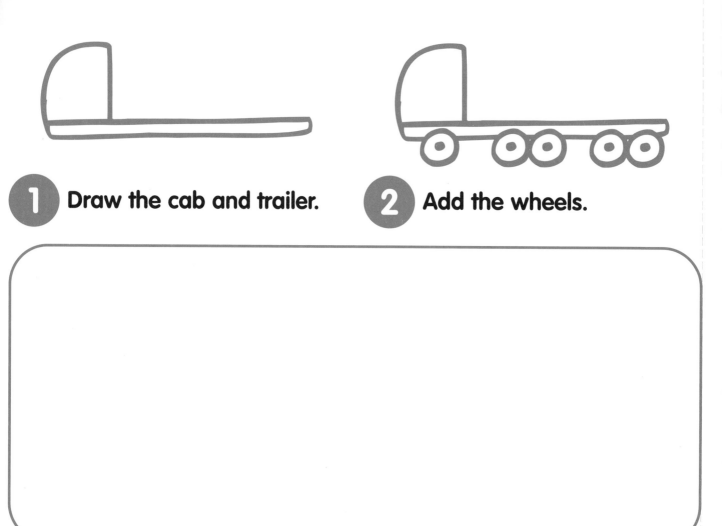

**1** Draw the cab and trailer.

**2** Add the wheels.

**3** Draw the large tank.

**4** Then add the headlight, window and finishing details.

# A speedboat has a powerful engine instead of sails.

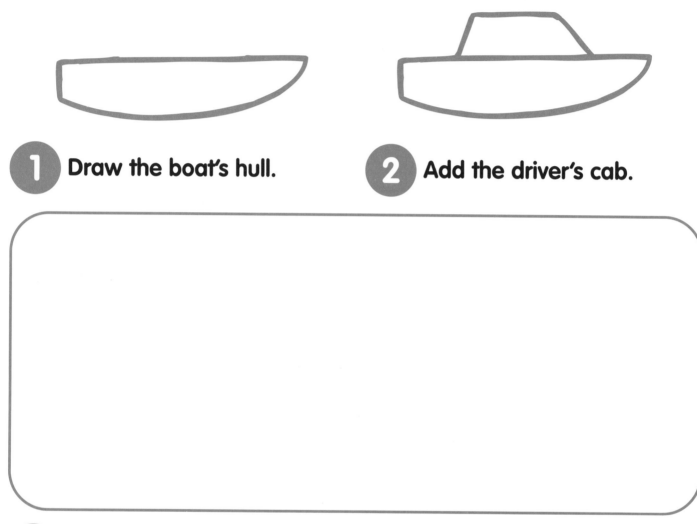

**1** Draw the boat's hull.

**2** Add the driver's cab.

**3** Draw the windows.

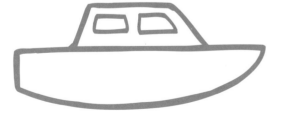

**4** Then add the flag and stripe.

# How much rubble can this dump truck carry?

**1** Draw the cab and trailer.

**2** Add the wheels.

**3** Draw the container.

**4** Then add the window, headlight and rubble.

# Jet planes dart through the sky!

**1** Draw the plane's shape.

**2** Add the wings.

**3** Draw the tail and engines.

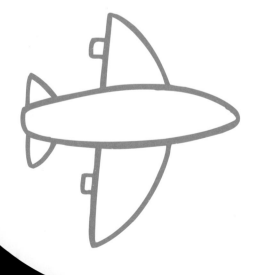

**4** Then add the windshield, tail stripe and windows.

# The submarine dives deep into the ocean.

**1** Draw the submarine's shape.

**2** Add the propeller.

**3** Draw the periscope.

**4** Then add the portholes and finishing details.

# Hot-air balloons fly high.

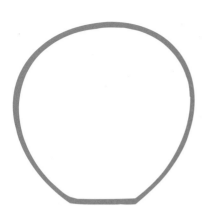

**1** Draw the balloon's shape.

**2** Add the ropes and basket.

**3** Draw the stripes and burner.

**4** Then add the finishing details.

# What is in the delivery van today?

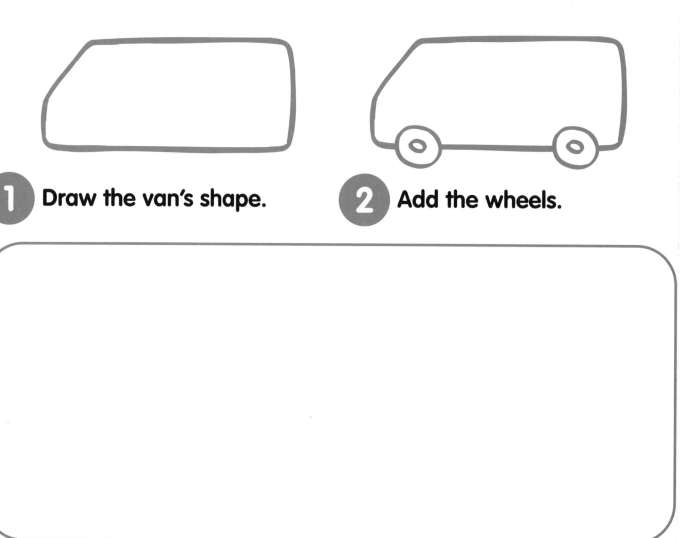

**1** Draw the van's shape.

**2** Add the wheels.

**3** Draw the driver's cab, window and headlight.

**4** Then add the finishing details.

# The ambulance hurries to the emergency.

**1** Draw the ambulance's shape.

**2** Add the wheels.

**3** Draw the windshield, stripe and headlight.

**4** Then add the flashing light and finishing details.

# How many wings are on a biplane?

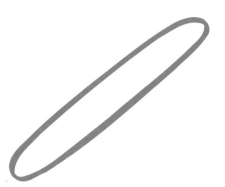

**1** Draw one wing.

**2** Add the plane shape under the wing.

**3** Draw the second wing and struts under the top wing.

**4** Then add the windshield and propeller.

# The police car rushes to the accident.

**1** Draw the car's shape.

**2** Add the wheels.

**3** Draw the windows and headlights.

**4** Then add the flashing light and finishing details.

# The windsurfer zips over the water.

**1** Draw the windsurfing board.

**2** Add the mast and sail.

**3** Draw the handlebar.

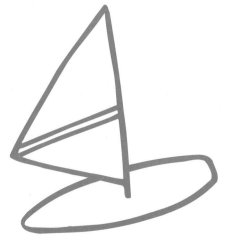

**4** Then add the finishing details.

# Tow trucks help broken-down cars.

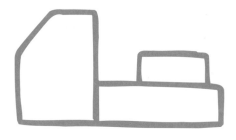

**1** Draw the driver's cab and the trailer.

**2** Add the wheels.

**3** Draw the crane.

**4** Then add the headlight, window and lifting hook.

# A tandem bicycle is for two people.

**1** Draw the tandem's frame.

**2** Add the wheels.

**3** Draw two seats.

**4** Then add two sets of pedals.

# This old car is perfect for days out.

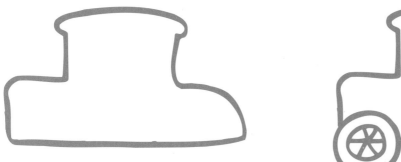

**1** Draw the car's shape.

**2** Add the wheels.

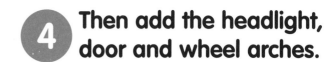

**3** Draw the windows and exhaust.

**4** Then add the headlight, door and wheel arches.

# A beach buggy is perfect for desert driving.

**1** Draw the buggy's shape.

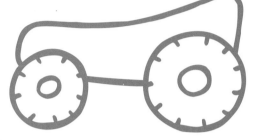

**2** Add the wheels.

**3** Draw the seat.

**4** Then add the steering wheel and finishing details.

# Use the truck to help move the house.

1 Draw the truck's shape.

2 Add the wheels.

3 Draw the driver's cab.

4 Then add the window, light and finishing details.

# Up and down mountains, this 4x4 can drive anywhere!

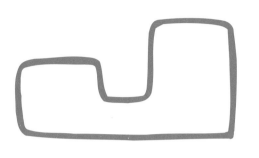

**1** Draw the vehicle's shape.

**2** Add the large wheels.

**3** Draw the headlight, spare tire and windshield.

**4** Then add the seat, window and tow bar.

# This snowmobile goes faster than the skiers.

**1** Draw the snowmobile's shape.

**2** Add the skis.

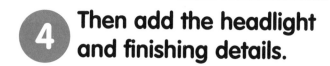

**3** Draw the seat.

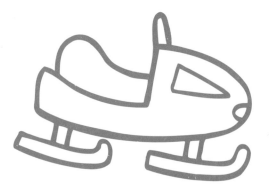

**4** Then add the headlight and finishing details.

# Gliders soar through the air like birds.

**1** Draw the glider's shape.

**2** Add the wings.

**3** Draw the tail.

**4** Then add the windshield.

# Row, row, row your boat, gently down the stream!

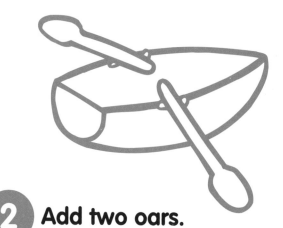

**1** Draw the boat's hull.

**2** Add two oars.

**3** Draw the seats.

**4** Then add the finishing details.

# How many logs can this truck carry?

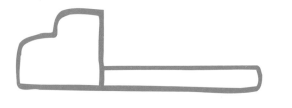

**1** Draw the driver's cab and trailer.

**2** Add the wheels.

**3** Draw the headlight, door and window.

**4** Then add the logs.

# Watch out! The bulldozer is clearing the rubble away.

**1** Draw an oval.

**2** Add three wheels inside.

**3** Draw the engine and driver's cab.

**4** Then add the scoop.

# Three, two, one, go!
# Which car will win the race?

**1** Draw the car's shape.

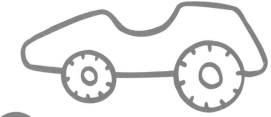

**2** Add the wheels.

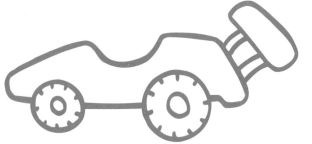

**3** Draw the spoiler.

**4** Then add the seat, light and finishing details.

# How many wheels does this tricycle have?

**1** Draw the tricycle's frame.

**2** Add one large wheel at the front.

**3** Draw two small wheels at the back.

**4** Then add the seat and pedals.

# This convertible is perfect for sunny days.

**1** Draw the car's shape.

**2** Add the wheels.

**3** Draw the windshield and roof.

**4** Then add the lights and door.

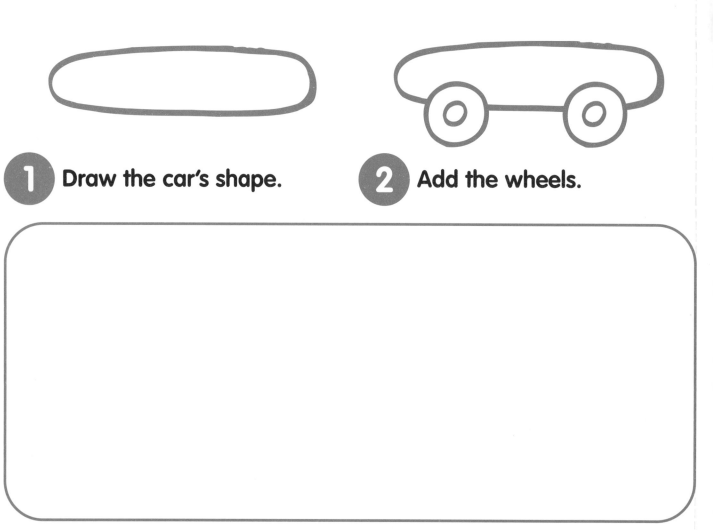

# This tugboat is powerful.

**1** Draw the boat's hull.

**2** Add the cabin and smokestack.

**3** Draw the portholes and smokestack stripes.

**4** Then add the barge and towing line.

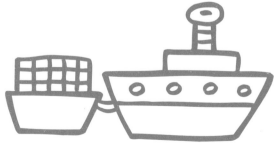

# Raise your hand
# and shout, "Taxi!"

**1** Draw the taxi's shape.

**2** Add the wheels.

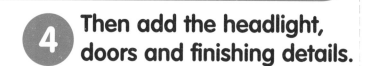

**3** Draw the windows.

**4** Then add the headlight, doors and finishing details.

# Clowns ride unicycles at the circus!

**1** Draw one large wheel.

**2** Add the frame.

**3** Draw the seat at the top.

**4** Then add the pedals.

# We love to sail
# on the sea in this yacht.

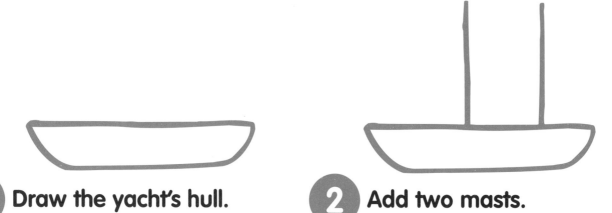

**1** Draw the yacht's hull.

**2** Add two masts.

**3** Draw the sails.

**4** Then add the flags and finishing details.

# Workers need the
# cement mixer to finish the house.

**1** Draw the driver's cab and the trailer.

**2** Add the wheels.

**3** Draw the mixing tank.

**4** Then add the headlight, window and finishing details.

# Who is inside this limousine?

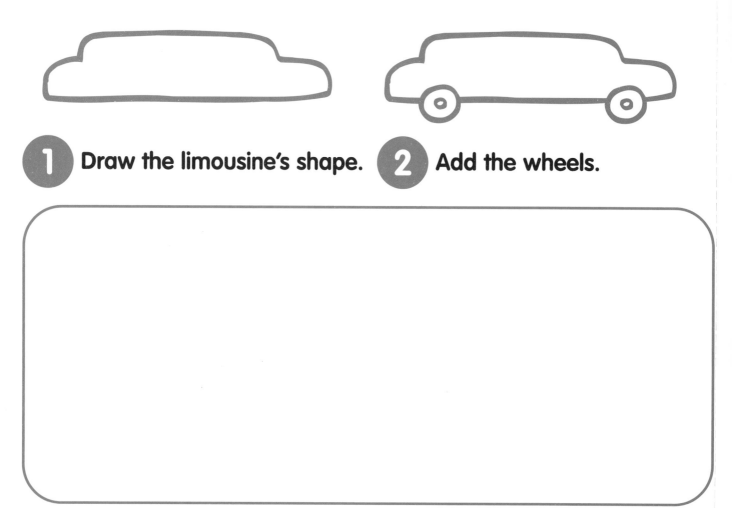

**1** Draw the limousine's shape.

**2** Add the wheels.

**3** Draw the windows.

**4** Then add the lights and finishing details.

# A seaplane can land on water!

**1** Draw one long wing.

**2** Add the plane underneath.

**3** Draw the landing skids.

**4** Then add the windshield and propeller.

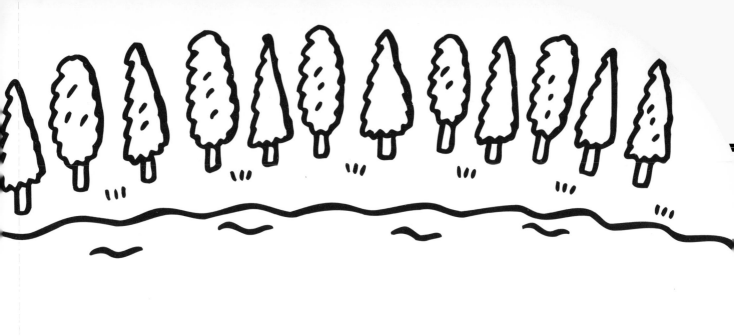

# A cruise ship takes people around the world.

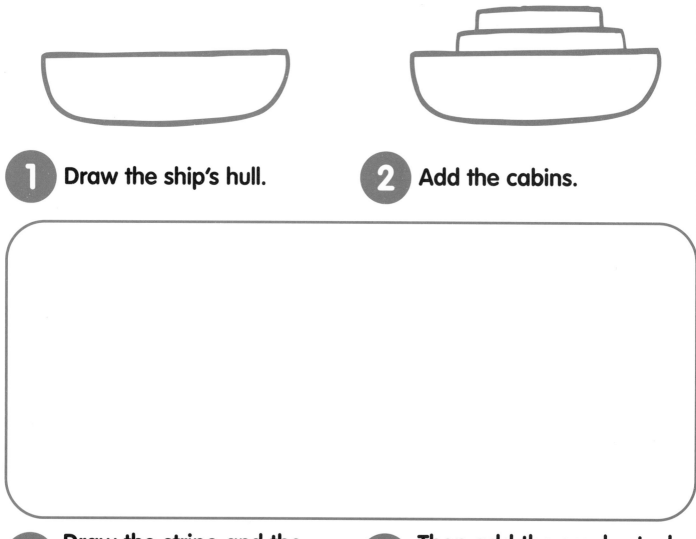

1 Draw the ship's hull.

2 Add the cabins.

3 Draw the stripe and the portholes.

4 Then add the smokestacks.

# The princess travels to the ball in this fairytale carriage.

**1** Draw the carriage's shape and door.

**2** Add the wheels.

**3** Draw the decorations.

**4** Then add the horse.

# Pirates sail the seas in their galleon.

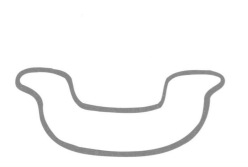

**1** Draw the ship's hull.

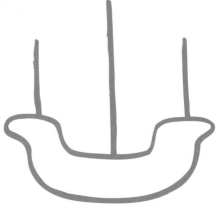

**2** Add three masts.

**3** Draw the sails.

**4** Then add the flags and finishing details.

# The toboggan swooshes over the snow.

**1** Draw the toboggan's shape.    **2** Add the legs.

**3** Draw two runners.    **4** Then add the finishing details.

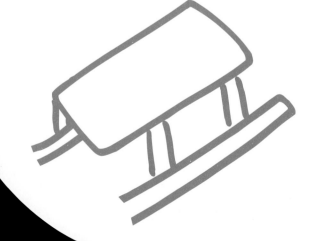
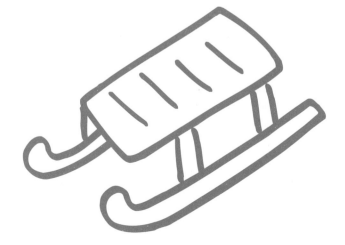

# The cable car glides high through the mountains.

**1** Draw a straight line and a square shape below it.

**2** Add the cable between the line and the square.

**3** Draw the grip mechanism.

**4** Then add the cable car windows and stripe.

# The car transporter carries lots of cars!

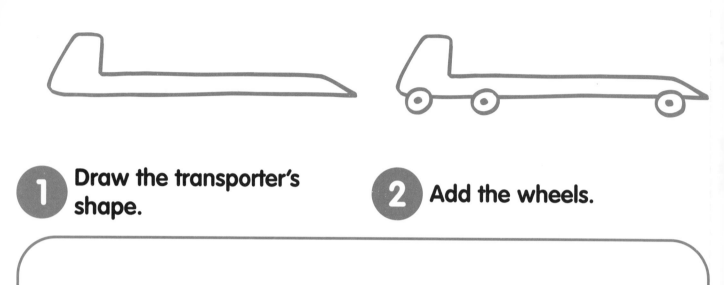

**1** Draw the transporter's shape.

**2** Add the wheels.

**3** Draw the headlight, window and car ramp.

**4** Then add the cars.

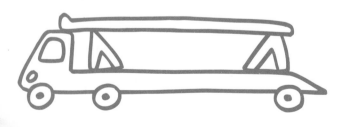

# You can travel and sleep in this motorhome.

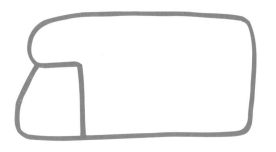

**1** Draw the motorhome's shape.

**2** Add the wheels.

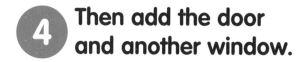

**3** Draw the window and headlights.

**4** Then add the door and another window.

# The lifeboat races to the rescue!

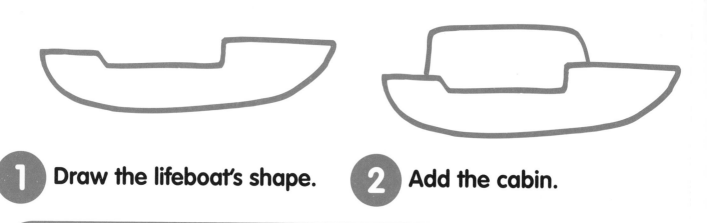

**1** Draw the lifeboat's shape.  **2** Add the cabin.

**3** Draw the windows.  **4** Draw the mast and life buoy.

# You can dig deep with this digger.

**1** Draw the digger's shape.

**2** Add the track and wheels.

**3** Draw the digger's arm.

**4** Then add the window, scoop and stripe.

# The hovercraft glides across the ocean.

**1** Draw the hovercraft's shape.  **2** Add two cabins.

**3** Draw the engines.

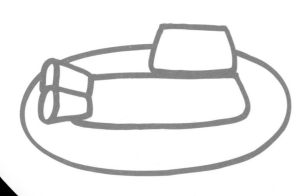

**4** Draw the windows, flag and finishing details.

# Lots of people travel on the subway.

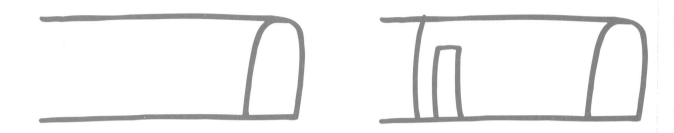

**1** Draw the train's shape.

**2** Add the door and stripe.

**3** Draw the wheels.

**4** Then add the windows and headlights.

# The steamroller
# makes the road flat.

**1** Draw the steamroller's shape.

**2** Add the wheel and the large roller.

**3** Draw the roller detail.

**4** Then add the windows.

# The combine harvester cuts the corn.

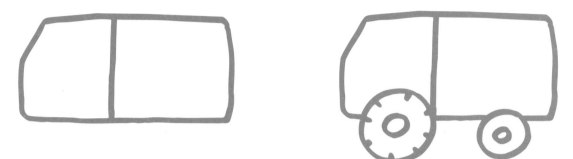

**1** Draw the harvester's shape.

**2** Add the one large and one small wheel.

**3** Draw the harvester mechanism.

**4** Draw the headlights and finishing details.

# Now doodle and draw your things that go!

# Now doodle and draw your things that go!

# Now doodle and draw your things that go!